Pets and People

ELDONNA L. EVERTTS
Language Arts

LYMAN C. HUNT
Reading

BERNARD J. WEISS
Linguistics and Curriculum

Edited by Jane Berkowitz and Craig Bettinger

Educational Consultants: Patsy Montague and Janet Sprout

THE HOLT BASIC READING SYSTEM
• LEVEL 5 •

HOLT, RINEHART AND WINSTON, INC.
New York / Toronto / London / Sydney

ACKNOWLEDGMENT

Grateful acknowledgment is given to G. P. Putnam's Sons for "The Goldfish" from *Everything and Anything* by Dorothy Aldis. Copyright 1925, 1926, 1927 by Dorothy Aldis. Reprinted by permission of the publisher.

ILLUSTRATED BY

Ethel Gold, pages 4–11, 31
Betty Fraser, pages 12–21
Ray Cruz, pages 22–29
Marilyn Bass Goldman, page 30
Lorraine Fox, pages 32–40
Diane de Groat, pages 41, 52–61
Jack Endewelt, pages 42–51
Viewpoint Graphics, Inc., page 62

ISBN 0-03-082852-X
3456789   071   98765432

Contents

4

Stop Gus!

Gus ran into a big store.

Sandy ran into the store.

"Stop, Gus," she said.

Gus didn't stop.

A big boy saw Gus.

"Stop," the big boy said.
"Come here, dog."

Gus didn't stop.
He ran out.

Two girls saw Gus.
The girls ran to stop Gus.
Gus didn't stop.

8

A little boy saw Gus.

"Here, dog," said the little boy.
"Good dog.
See the cookies?"

Gus saw the cookies.

What did he do?

He ran to the little boy.

The big boy and the girls saw Gus.

What did they do?

They ran to Gus and the boy.

Sandy didn't stop Gus.

The big boy didn't stop Gus.

The two girls didn't stop Gus.

The cookies did!

What Can You Do with a Burro?

"Come and see my burro," said Pablo.

The boys and girls ran with Pablo.
They ran to see the burro.

"He is a good burro," said a boy.
"What can you do with a burro?"

15

"Here," said Pablo.

"You can play with a burro."

Pablo ran up to the burro.

The burro didn't play.

16

"The burro won't play," said a girl.

"What **can** you do with a burro?"

"You can do a trick," said Pablo.

"My burro will do a trick."

The burro didn't do the trick.

"The burro won't play," said a boy.

"The burro won't do the trick.

What can you do with a burro?"

Pablo ran to the burro.

"You can love a burro," he said.

And he did!

Pablo Has a Donkey

Pablo has a donkey
His ears go floppy-flop!
It's hard to get him started,
It's hard to make him stop!

Pablo's beast is stubborn,
He balks at every hill,
At times he's very trying
But Pablo loves him still!

—Nona Keen Duffy

Big Sister and Little Brother

"Come with me," said Big Sister.
"Come into the house.
You will see my three goldfish."

The girls ran into the house.

They ran to see the goldfish.

Big Sister saw the goldfish bowl.

She didn't see three goldfish.

She saw two goldfish!

Where was the big goldfish?

Big Sister saw Little Brother.

"Little Brother!" she said.

"Where is my goldfish?"

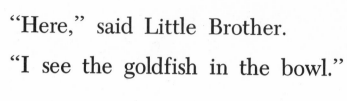

"Here," said Little Brother.
"I see the goldfish in the bowl."

"One is not here," said Big Sister.
"Where is the big goldfish?"

"Here is the big goldfish.

It's in the bowl!" said Little Brother.

The Goldfish

My darling little goldfish
Hasn't any toes;
He swims around without a sound
And bumps his hungry nose.

He can't get out to play with me,
Nor I get in to him,
Although I say: "Come out and play,"
And he—"Come in and swim."

—Dorothy Aldis

Making New Words

ran	it	did	up	Ben
rag	if	dig	us	bed

Gus ran with the rag.

Ben went to bed.

See us up here.

Did Rex like to dig?

Jill will read the book if she likes it.

Final Consonant Substitution. Have each pair of words read, calling attention to the final consonant substitution in the second word. Then have the sentences read.

Shep, the Sheep Dog

Shep was a sheep dog.

He was a good sheep dog.

"Come here, Shep!" said Tim.
"I do not see my little sheep.
Go find it, Shep."

Shep went to find the little sheep.

He saw the little sheep.

The sheep ran and ran.

Shep ran and ran.

The little sheep went into the water.

Shep saw the sheep in the water.

He went in to get the sheep.

Tim ran to find Shep.

He saw Shep in the water.

He saw the little sheep in the water.

38

"Come out, Shep," said Tim.

"Make the little sheep come out."

"Good dog," said Tim.

"You are a good sheep dog."

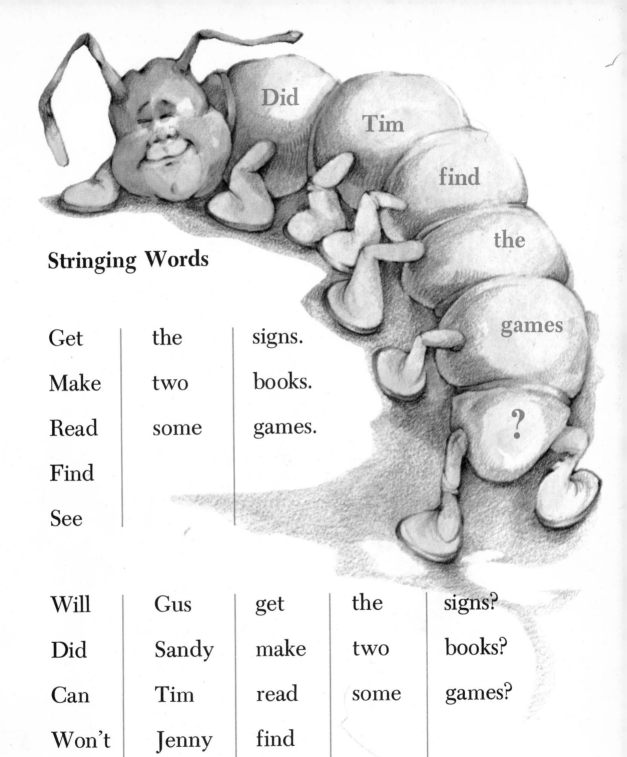

Stringing Words

Get	the	signs.
Make	two	books.
Read	some	games.
Find		
See		

Will	Gus	get	the	signs?
Did	Sandy	make	two	books?
Can	Tim	read	some	games?
Won't	Jenny	find		
		see		

41

Sentence Patterns. Have the children choose a word from each column to form sentences.

Bluebell, the Cow

A little boy was in the house.

"I want to play," he said.

"I will get my brother."

The little boy ran to get his brother.

"Play with me," said the little boy.

"No," said his brother.
"I want to play with my dog."

The little boy ran to his sister.

"Will you play with me?" he asked.

"No," said his sister.

"I want to read my book."

"What can I do?" asked the little boy.

The little boy saw Bluebell.

He ran to the cow.

"I will make Bluebell play," he said.

And up he went.

"Get up, Bluebell," said the boy.

"Get up and play with me.

Go, Bluebell, go."

The boy didn't make Bluebell go.

"Here comes my sister," said the boy.

"She will make you go."

"Come down," said his sister.

"You won't make the cow go."

"What can she do?" asked the boy.

"See," said the girl.

"Here is what a cow can do."

The Cow

The friendly cow all red and white,
I love with all my heart:
She gives me cream
   with all her might,
To eat with apple tart.

—Robert Louis Stevenson

Who Is It?

A little girl went to see Kolo.
She went to his house.

"Kolo, Kolo," she said.
"Come out and play."

"Who is it?" asked someone.

"It's Neko," said the girl.
"I want to play with Kolo."

"Who is it?" asked someone again.

"Neko," said the girl.

"I want Kolo to come out."

"Who is it?" asked someone.

"It's Neko," said the girl again.
"Will you get Kolo?
I want to play with Kolo."

Neko saw Kolo come to the house.

"Here you are," said Neko.
"I want you to come and play.
Who is in the house?"

"No one is in the house," said Kolo.

"Someone asked, 'Who is it?'
Someone **is** in the house," said Neko.

"Come with me," said Kolo.

"You will see who it is."

Kolo and Neko went into the house.

"Someone **is** here," said Kolo.

"And here he is!"

Putting Words Together

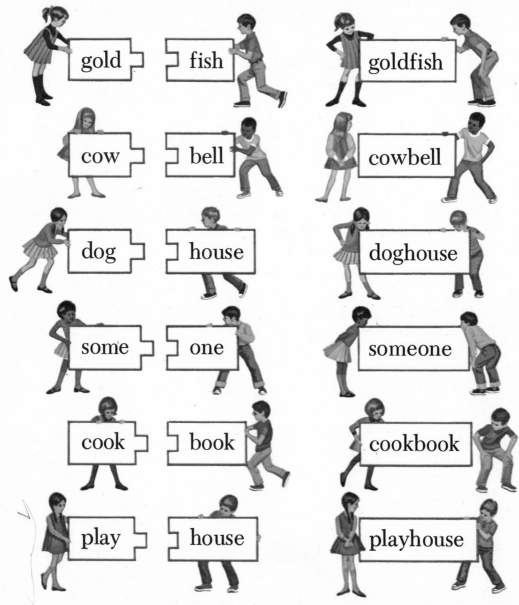

gold fish goldfish

cow bell cowbell

dog house doghouse

some one someone

cook book cookbook

play house playhouse

Compound Words. Have children read the word held by the girl
and the word held by the boy. Then have the compound word read.

Stringing Words

Tim The boy He	likes	games.
Jenny The girl She	makes	cookies.
Jim and Dan The boys They	see	someone.
Jill and Sandy The girls They	play	here.

Sentence Patterns. Have the children choose a word or words from each column to form sentences.

63

New Words

The words listed beside the page numbers below are introduced in *Pets and People*, Level 5 in THE HOLT BASIC READING SYSTEM.

5. stop	18. will	36. went
Gus	20. love	37. water
6. Sandy	23. sister	get
ran	brother	43. Bluebell
didn't	24. goldfish	cow
7. saw	26. bowl	44. want
he	was	his
13. can	28. I	45. no
with	29. it's	46. asked
burro	33. Shep	54. Kolo
14. my	sheep	55. Neko
Pablo	35. Tim	56. again
17. won't		